GW00385141

MULTIPLE-CHOICE

ENGLISH

Practice Test 1

Guidance for completing this Test.

1.   Read the passages carefully.

2.   Read the questions thoroughly.

3.   Read the answers carefully.

4.   Choose what you think is the correct answer carefully.

5.   Underline or circle the answer, immediately after the

        question.

6.   Transfer the LETTER **A,B,C,D,E** or **N** to the answer sheet.

7.   Make sure to mark the answer box like [—] not [╱].

8.   Check carefully that you have transferred your correct answer.

9 .   This test lasts for **50 minutes.**

PUPIL'S NAME _____

TOTAL MARK
(Out of 60)

Read this passage and answer the questions which follow.
If there are any words you don't understand you may find
them in the Glossary at the end of the test.

CHRISTMAS EVE

1.   At last, Christmas Eve dawned. We brought in the holly which
we had collected from the field the previous Saturday and very soon
holly branches seemed to be growing out of every picture and
everywhere else; apart from our precious grandfather clock which
5. was my father's pride and joy and could not be touched.
        Then came the ceremony of the Christmas tree. There was
a forest of evergreen trees, planted by my father, around our house.
He seemed to love every tree as he had great difficulty in selecting
the tree which was to decorate our house.
10.   He usually picked a tree that was lop-sided or missing
branches but when we had decorated it with our cards, balloons
and homemade baubles it was a real beauty. We made our own
streamers out of coloured paper and newspapers and painted these
to be hung in lines across the ceiling of the kitchen.
15.   While we decorated the kitchen, Mother made the
preparations for the Christmas dinner. To provide the light for the
window we cleaned out a large turnip and made a hole in it for the
candle. We decorated this with berried holly and placed it in the
window. That night no blinds would be drawn so that the light
20. would shine out to light the way for Joseph and Mary.
        Before supper the Christmas log was brought in and put
behind the fire in the open hearth. Banked around with lumps of
turf it sent out a glow of warmth to make the toast which was part of
our Christmas tradition.
25.   Before anything could be eaten the Christmas candle had to be
lit. We gathered round as my mother sprinkled it with holy water
and my father lit the candle. We all sat round the table with Father
at the head of the table and the rest of us in our usual places.
        I feasted my eyes on the white iced cake, the seed loaf and the
30. barm brack but most of all I stared at the mountain of golden toast
oozing with yellow butter. After supper we had lemonade and
biscuits and the ecstacy of the fizzy lemonade bubbling down my
nose remains a memory that is Christmas for me.
        Our gramophone was normally kept safe in the parlour but at
35. the festive season it was brought into the kitchen. My father bought
new records every Christmas and they were played non-stop. But
the records stopped when the radio was turned on for the news.

1.

If the night was very cold we had a fire which cast magical
shadows along the low timber ceiling while the moon shone fingers
40. of light across the floor. Anything seemed possible. Try as I did to
keep my eyes open to see Santa appear out of the shadows, I was
soon carried into the world of sleep and very soon, it seemed, I was
awake and felt the anticipation of seeing what Santa had brought.
No sensation in later life could compare with the boundless joy of
45. those early Christmas mornings when Santa was a reality.

**Answer the following questions. Look back over the passage.
You should choose the _best_ answer and mark its letter on
your answer sheet.**

1.   Which of the following is **true** ?

A.   This story tells the story of Christmas.
B.   This story is about the commercialisation of Christmas.
C.   This story is about a family's preparation for Christmas.
D.   This story is about Santa Claus.
E.   This story is about a child's bad memories of Christmas.

2.   What kind of tree did the father select for Christmas ?

A.   He selected a deciduous tree.
B.   He selected a green tree.
C.   He selected a tree that was perfectly symmetrical.
D.   He selected a tree that had holly on it.
E.   He selected a tree that wasn't straight, with boughs missing.

3.   What **food** did the family have after supper ?

A.   Potatoes and vegetables.
B.   Fizzy lemonade and biscuits.
C.   Golden toast covered in yellow butter.
D.   Barm brack and seed loaf.
E.   Turkey and ham.

4.   What made shadows on the kitchen ceiling ?

A.   The light from the tilley lamp.
B.   The candles in the windows.
C.   The flames from the fire.
D.   The electric light on the ceiling.
E.   The light from the moon.

2.

5. In the **last paragraph** what was the author looking forward to when the author awoke ?

A. Seeing what presents Santa had brought.
B. Seeing Santa coming out of the shadows.
C. Seeing the flames from the fire.
D. Watching the snow falling in the garden.
E. Hearing the news on radio.

6. Which of the following **best** describes the decorations used in the house.

A. Homemade cards, balloons, baubles and white streamers.
B. Homemade baubles, cards, balloons and coloured streamers.
C. Homemade balloons, cards, baubles and white streamers.
D. Homemade mistletoe, cards, baubles and balloons.
E. Homemade tree, cards, balloons and coloured newspapers.

7. In which places were holly bushes placed ?

A. Behind doors, on the ceiling and beside the fire.
B. On the table, on shelves and on the pictures.
C. On the streamers, on the walls and windows.
D. Everywhere, except on the clock.
E. Beside the sofa, around the chairs and around the lamp.

8. Why were the blinds on the windows **not** drawn?

A. To allow the electric light to shine out on to the street.
B. To allow the light to light the way for Joseph and Mary.
C. So that Mary and Joseph could call at the house.
D. Because they were covered with berried holly.
E. So that the family could see their way around the house.

9. How was the bread toasted for the Christmas Eve supper ?

A. In the electric toaster.
B. By the heat and light from the candles.
C. Under the grill in the oven.
D. In front of the electric fire.
E. In front of the turf fire.

3.

10. Where was the family's record-player normally kept?

A. It was stored in a box in the kitchen.
B. It sat on a shelf in the sitting room.
C. It was kept in a wardrobe in the bedroom.
D. It was kept safe in the parlour.
E. It was kept safe in the kitchen.

The following passage contains a number of mistakes. You have to find the mistakes. On each line there is either _one_ mistake or _no_ mistake. Find the group of words in which there is a mistake and mark the letter for it on your answer sheet. If there is no mistake, mark N.
First, look for the _spelling_ mistakes.

11. Having woked | mother and | father to show | them Santa's
         A   B   C   D   N

12. genarosity we | all set out to | walk the three | miles to church.
         A   B   C   D   N

13. This morning | was different | from others as | candles glowed
         A   B   C   D   N

14. in every | window of the | farmhouses dotted | along the root.
         A   B   C   D   N

15. Seeing the | crib decerated | and full of figures | added to the
         A   B   C   D   N

16. magic of the | morning as did | the return journey | home in hour
         A   B   C   D   N

17. neighbur's horse | and trap. For breakfast we | had baked ham
         A   B   C   D   N

18. and homemade | wheeten bread | and afterwards | mother set
         A   B   C   D   N

19. about puting | the stuffed goose | in the big metal | pot, covered
         A   B   C   D   N

20. it with a lid and | covered the lid | with hot coals | from the fire.
         A   B   C   D   N

Now look for _punctuation_ mistakes.

There the pot rested as the delicious aroma from the pot filled the kitchen as we children played joyously with

21. our new toys | and squealed | and giggled | with delight. | N
     A | B | C | D

22. " i am delighted | with my new | doll," shrieked | Mary as | N
     A | B | C | D

23. danny played | with his | new tractor | and trailer. | N
     A | B | C | D

24. Both the radio | and the record | player we're | on but when | N
     A | B | C | D

25. it was time | for dinner ? | we all fell silent | and gathered | N
     A | B | C | D

26. round the table | for the feast | of feasts. what | a wonderful | N
     A | B | C | D

27. Christmas | we had. The | trees decorations | still looked | N
     A | B | C | D

28. magnificent! | and the candle | also burned | brightly. | N
     A | B | C | D

Read this passage and answer the questions which follow. If there are any words you don't understand you may find them in the Glossary at the end of the test.

FLIGHTY BIRD

1   I don't know if I slept that night, but I was up and out before sunrise, and, taking the cage, set out to look for my bird, with little hope of finding him, for there were foxes in that place - a family of cubs which I had seen - and, worse still the large blood-thirsty
5.   weasels of that country.

5.

But no sooner was I at the spot where I had lost him than I was greeted with his loud note and there he was hopping out from among the thistles, a most forlorn looking object, his plummage wet and bedraggled, and his feet covered with wet clay ! And he was
10. glad to see me ! As soon as I left the cage down he came straight to it, and without a moment's hesitation, hopped in and began feasting on the seed. It was a happy ending.

My bird had had a lesson which he would not forget; there would be no more tugging at the wires, nor would he ever wish to be
15. free again. So I imagined. But I was wrong. From that time the bird's disposition was changed; ever in a restless anxious state, he would flit from side to side of the cage, chirping loudly but never singing - never one note; the gladness that had made him sing songs wonderfully had quite gone out of him.
20. And invariably, after hopping about for a few moments, he would go back to the wire which had loosened and bent - the one weak spot which was now repaired - and tug and shake it again. And at last, greatly to my surprise, he actually succeeded in bending the same wire once more and making his escape !
25. Once more I went to look for him with the cage in my hand, but when I found him he refused to be tempted. I left him for a day to starve, then tried him again many and many times on many following days, for he was much too strong on the wing to be hunted down; but though he invariably greeted me with his loud chirp, he
30. refused to come down, and after excitedly hailing me and flirting with his feathers for a few moments he would fly away.

Gradually I grew resigned to my loss, for, though no longer my captive - my own bird - he was near me, living in the plantation and frequently seen.

Answer the following questions. Look back over the passage. You should choose the _best_ answer and mark its letter on your answer sheet. Using the passage, select the correct ending to the following 6 sentences.

29.   In the **first paragraph** of the story, the bird

A.   had escaped.
C.   was eaten by black weasels.
E.   was lying dead in his cage.
B.   was happy in the cage.
D.   was eaten by foxes.

30.   In the **first paragraph** of the story, the owner of the bird was

A.   anxious but hopeful.
C.   angry but hopeful.
E.   desperate and hopeless.
B.   unconcerned and content.
D.   happy and eager.

6.

31. After the bird was recaptured in the **second paragraph** it was

A. less comfortable but happy.   B. hungry and bedraggled.
C. comfortable but restless.   D. annoyed and dirty.
E. comfortable and healthy.

32. When the bird returned to its cage in **line 13**, the owner thought that

A. the bird would escape again.
B. the bird would sing for ever.
C. the bird's hunger would ensure that it would fly away.
D. the bird would never want to escape again.
E. the door of the cage could be left open.

33. In **paragraph 3** the bird seemed to sing only

A. when it was hungry.   B. when it was happy.
C. when it was anxious.   D. when it had enough food.
E. when it was out of the cage.

34. At the end of the story

A. the pet was recaptured.
B. the bird was the man's friend, but no longer his pet.
C. the bird was free and frequently seen.
D. the man completely lost contact with the bird.
E. the owner bought another bird.

35. Which animals might have harmed the bird ?

A. hawks and eagles   B. wolves and foxes
C. weasels and fox cubs   D. cubs and scouts
E. thistles and nettles

36. Which activities did the bird partake in when it was in an unsettled and uneasy state ?

A. eating seeds and grass   B. hopping about and chirping
C. singing and sleeping   D. flapping and biting
E. flying and jumping

37. On the last attempt that the owner made to recapture the bird
what was the outcome of the attempt ?

A. The bird happily walked into the cage.
B. The bird flew around and then sat on top of the cage.
C. The owner and the bird were friendly and the bird stayed.
D. The bird greeted its owner but refused to go into the cage.
E. The bird stayed up in the trees and didn't move.

38. Which of the following is closest in meaning to the phrase
"much too strong on the wing" in **lines 28 and 29** ?

A. ...able to open the cage with its wing.
B. ...too strong to eat its food.
C. ...able to fly expertly.
D. ...able to be caught easily.
E. ...unable to fly capably.

39. Which of the following is the best meaning for the
word, **"bedraggled"** as used in **line 9** ?

A. dragged along the ground   B. sweating from head to foot
C. clean and neat and tidy   D. dirty and covered in mud
E. prim and proper

40. The word **"invariably "** is used in **line 20** to describe how the bird
would go back to the wire of the cage.
Which of the following is the best meaning for **"invariably"** ?

A. always   B. permanently
C. occasionally   D. carefully
E. speedily

41. The word **"forlorn"** is used in **line 8** to describe how the bird looked
when he was first found.
Which of the following is the best meaning for **"forlorn"** ?

A. ...happy and excited.
B. ...wretched and down in the dump.
C. ...sorrowful and forgiving.
D. ...well-mannered and regretful.
E. ...hopeful and expectant.

8.

42. How did the bird escape from the cage ?

A. The bird opened the cage door and flew out.
B. The bird's owner opened the cage and let him out.
C. The bird found a loose wire and bent it to make a hole.
D. The cage fell over and the bird escaped.
E. The owner left the door open by mistake and the bird escaped.

Read this passage and answer the questions which follow. If there are any words you don't understand you may find them in the Glossary at the end of the test.

GERMS

1.   When people catch a disease like diptheria or tetanus it is because some tiny living things, called *microbes* (or 'germs') have got inside our bodies. Germs in our bodies can damage us and poison us. They may attack animals and plants as well. An attack

5.   by germs is called an *infection*.

Cells

The bodies of animals and plants are made up of millions of tiny parts, called *cells*. Cells are invisible to our eyes. They have to be looked at and photographed through a microscope, which will magnify the picture. ('Magnify' means 'make bigger').

10.   Our skin and muscles and bones are made up of cells. When we grow, the number of cells in our bodies gets greater and greater, until we are fully grown. Cells can split in two, so that there are two cells where there was only one before. If each of these cells splits in two, that will make four cells. If each of them splits in

15.   two, that will make eight. Soon there will be thousands and thousands.

Kinds of germ

There are two main kinds of germ. One is the *bacterium*, and the other is the *virus*. There are many different viruses and many different bacteria. ('Bacteria' is the plural of 'bacterium.') Bacteria

20.   and viruses are unlike one another in some important ways.

Bacteria

A bacterium has only one cell. It can split in two, just as the cells in our bodies do when we are growing. But when the bacteria split, they become separate living things. They do not stay as parts of one body.

25.   Bacteria often grow very fast. So even if there are only a few to start with, there can soon be millions of them. We say that bacteria *multiply rapidly*.

30. Some kinds of bacteria can give people a sore throat. Doctors can rub a little stick called a **swab** on the person's throat and send the swab to a hospital laboratory to have the bacteria identified.

They will know what kind of medicine to give. They may give a drug called an *antibiotic* to kill bacteria.

Other bacteria, called *salmonella,* are found in some kinds of raw meat, especially chicken meat. If they are eaten alive, they give
35. people food poisoning, but they are killed when the meat is cooked.

Chickens need to be very well cooked because many of the bacteria are inside.

Viruses

A virus is much smaller than a bacterium, and much smaller than the cells in our bodies. Viruses cannot be seen through an
40. ordinary microscope. A very special kind of microscope is needed.

Unlike bacteria, viruses can go right inside the cells of our bodies. They live inside the cells and damage them, so that we become unwell. We become infected with the virus.

43. According to the passage which of the following statements is **true** ?

A. Infection is caused by eating raw meat.
B. Infection is caused by washing in dirty water.
C. Infection is caused by holding hands.
D. Infection is caused by germs getting into our bodies.
E. Infection is caused by attack from animals and plants.

44. Which of the following statements is **true** according to the passage ?

A. All germs are harmful.　　　　B. Some germs are harmful.
C. Only bacteria are harmful.　　D. Only viruses are harmful.
E. The passage doesn't tell us whether all germs are harmful.

45. How would **diptheria** and **tetanus** be described ?

A. They are bacteria.　　　　B. They are germs.
C. They are viruses.　　　　D. They are medicines.
E. They are diseases.

46. Which of the following is the **singular** of of bacteria ?

A. Bacter.　　　　B. Bacteria.　　　　C. Bactera.
D. Bacterium.　　　E. Bacteri.

10.

47. According to the passage which of the following statements is **true** ?

A. On average, there are more cells in an adult's body than in the body of a child.
B. On average, there are more cells in a child's body than in the body of an adult.
C. Plants have more cells than animals.
D. Animals have more cells than plants.
E. An adult has the same number of cells as a child.

48. What is used to test a person for a sore throat ?

A. A swab of a virus is taken from the person's throat and sent to a laboratory.
B. The person takes a sample from their throat and sends it to a laboratory.
C. A swab of a virus is taken from the person's ear and sent to a laboratory.
D. A swab of bacteria is taken from the person's throat and sent to a laboratory.
E. The person is tested and sent to the hospital.

49. Why has chicken meat to be **thoroughly cooked** ?

A. To get the best flavour from the meat.
B. To destroy the cells in the meat.
C. To cook the salmonella.
D. To kill the harmful bacteria that might be in the meat.
E. To give the people who eat it food poisoning.

50. How do viruses make a person become **unwell** ?

A. They live on the person's skin.
B. They live in a microscope and damage the person.
C. The person swallows the virus.
D. They grow on the outside of the cells in the person's body.
E. They go right inside the cells of the person and damage them.

51. What happens when bacteria divide ?

A. They make people unwell.
B. They give people food poisoning.
C. They stay as part of the body.
D. They become separate living things.
E. They grow very slowly.

52. How is salmonella killed ?

A. When food is cleaned.   B. When food is chilled.
C. When food is eaten raw.   D. When food is well cooked.
E. When food is left out in the open.

53. Which word in the passage means the same as :-
germs that are smaller than bacteria ?

A. Viruses.   B. Salmonella.   C. Germs.
D. Microscope.   E. Cells.

54. The main **emphasis** in the **first paragraph** entitled GERMS is

A. Cells are made up of millions of germs.
B. Germs can be easily seen with our eyes.
C. Germs only attack humans.
D. Germs can attack and damage plants, animals and humans.
E. Germs are the means whereby illnesses are cured.

55. How do the cells in our bodies **increase** ?

A. Our bodies react to an antibiotic.
B. Bacteria grow and multiply.
C. Each cell splits in two and this process continues.
D. They grow on our skins and in our bones.
E. They are attacked by bacteria and viruses.

General Section

To answer these questions, you may have to think about the passages you have read. Look back at these if you need to. Look also at the Index and Glossary.

56. (a) Proper Nouns

A. begin with a small letter.
C. begin all sentences.

B. begin with a capital letter.
D. take the place of pronouns.

(b). In which of the stories would you find poetry writing ?

A. CHRISTMAS EVE.
C. GERMS

B. FLIGHTY BIRD.
D. None of the three.

57. (a) What is the purpose of the **GLOSSARY** ?

A. To provide a list of the pages in the booklet.
B. To show the titles of each passage and their page numbers.
C. To give explanations of difficult words.
D. To list the names and addresses of the characters.

(b). Which word in the glossary means the same as **'temperament'** ?

A. plummage
C. disposition

B. medicine
D. anticipation

58. (a) For what can you use the **Index** ?

A. Gives a list of the difficult words.
B. Shows the reader where to find other similar passages.
C. Referring the reader to particular parts in the booklet.
D. Finding the definitions of difficult words.

(b). **"If the night was very cold we had a fire which cast magical shadows along the low timber ceiling while the moon shone fingers of light across the floor."**
These lines are taken from the first passage,**"Christmas Eve"**.
Which **three words** are Adjectives ?

A. night, fire and shadows
C. cold, magical, low

B. while, floor, shone
D. was, cast, across

59. (a) In which publication would you most likely find the passage entitled **"GERMS"** ?

A. a geography text book
B. a medical text book
C. a dictionary or thesaurus
D. a diary

(b). What **part of speech** could be described as the **particular** names of people, places animals or things ?

A. Pronouns
B. Proper nouns
C. Collective nouns
D. Common nouns

60. (a) Which phrase from the last paragraph of the passage, **"Christmas Eve"** means the same as **"being aware of the expectation of glimpsing"** ?

A. ..shone fingers of light...
B. ..felt the anticipation of seeing...
C. ..try as I did to keep my eyes open...
D. ..could compare with the boundless joy...

(b). **"If the night was very cold we had a fire which cast magical shadows along the low timber ceiling while the moon shone fingers of light across the floor."** These are **lines 38 to 40** taken from the passage, **"Christmas Eve".**
What does this tell us ?

A. That the moon was the only means of light.
B. That the fire was the only means of light.
C. That a fire was lit when the night was cold.
D. That the family couldn't afford a proper light.

GLOSSARY

evergreen----- having leaves all year long
baubles-------- trinkets and decorations for a Christmas tree
hearth--------- the floor part of a fireplace
fizzy---------- small bubbles of liquid spray up
gramophone-- old-fashioned record player
anticipation- expectation and foresight
weasels------- small mammals, long bodies, tails and short legs
plummage----- bird's feathers
disposition---- character, personality, spirit
captive-------- caged, imprisoned, restricted
microscope--- an instrument to enlarge the image of small objects
plural----------more than one of anything
swab----------- small piece of cotton wool or other material to clean
a wound or take a sample from a patient's body
medicine-------liquid or tablets used to treat disease

INDEX

NEW TRANSFER TESTS

MULTIPLE-CHOICE

ENGLISH

Practice Test 2

Guidance for completing this Test.

1.   Read the passages carefully.

2.   Read the questions thoroughly.

3.   Read the answers carefully.

4.   Choose what you think is the correct answer carefully.

5.   Underline or circle the answer, immediately after the
     question.

6.   Transfer the LETTER **A,B,C,D,E** or **N** to the answer sheet.

7.   Make sure to mark the answer box like [—] not [✓].

8.   Check carefully that you have transferred your correct answer.

9 .   This test lasts for **50 minutes.**

PUPIL'S NAME _____

TOTAL MARK (Out of 60)	

Read this passage and answer the questions which follow. If there are any words you don't understand you may find them in the Glossary at the end of the test.

DRAMA HISTORY

1.   The origins of drama and theatre probably go back to the beginning of civilisation. A father and son returning from a day's hunting might act out the hunt to entertain the other members of the family. The father or son would play the part of the bear,
5.   wearing the bear skin to make the show more realistic.

        If the actors were good, the other members of the tribe would want to see the bear hunt acted out again and again. Perhaps as time went on, extra scenes might be put in to make it even more exciting or to make those watching laugh. When the acting out of
10.   the bear hunt became even more popular it would be performed at a particular place - probably a piece of flat ground at the foot of a hill, from where the entire community could see the action. Such events may have been the beginnings of theatre in early society.

        The history of theatre and drama as we know it today began in
15.   Greece. The word theatre comes from the Greek word meaning "a seeing place". Almost three thousand years ago plays and drama formed part of religious services in Greece. A wooden platform was built at the bottom of a convenient hillside. The people who watched sat on wooden benches or stone steps built one behind the other up
20.   the hillside. The actors performed on a wooden stage on the back of which a changing room or *skene* was built. The front of the *skene* would be decorated and so we get the word *scenery* from *skene*. The plays told stories of the gods and of the exploits of legendary heroes. They used primitive cranes to lower actors, playing the parts
25.   of gods, to the stage.

        The inspiration for the Roman theatre came from Greece but the Romans introduced some new developments. They staged plays that dealt with the lives of ordinary people instead of telling stories of gods and heroes. They introduced a curtain across the front of
30.   the stage and used trap-doors and other mechanical effects. Over the period of the Roman empire, theatre was a popular form of entertainment and the remains of Roman theatres still survive today.

        The fall of the Roman Empire in the sixth century resulted in
35.   the decline of theatre in Europe. Actors and musicians were forced to take to the roads, performing plays at fairs and at other events where people gathered. Throughout the next five centuries, bands of wandering minstrels and actors travelled from town to town

reciting tales of adventure and performing simple comedy sketches.
40. By the eleventh century, minstrels and actors were being engaged
     by noblemen to provide entertainment at banquets.
          The church began to change its attitude recognising that
     drama was a way of bringing the parables and the stories in the
     Bible to reality for their congregations. Simple plays were staged in
45. churches to celebrate on major feast days - the Nativity scene at
     Christmas, the Last Supper at Easter. As these productions grew
     in appeal larger productions were needed and churches hadn't the
     facilities so various organisations set up what were called *guilds*.

**Answer the following questions. Look back over the passage.
You should choose the _best_ answer and mark its letter on your
answer sheet.**

1. Which of the following is **TRUE** ?

A. Theatre as we know it today began in England.
B. Theatre as we know it today began in Hollywood.
C. Theatre as we know it today began in Rome.
D. Theatre as we know it today began in Greece.
E. Theatre as we know it today began in Europe.

2. The **earliest** plays or dramas took place

A. ...on a stage in a theatre with an audience.
B. ...in the open on flat ground beside a hill.
C. ...on a platform at fairs or other events in front of a lot of people
D. ...in parks in large cities.
E. ...in brightly lit studios on TV.

3. The **earliest** plays or dramas were based on

A. ...books and manuscripts written by local people.
B. ...ideas that came from students of drama and theatre
C. ...historical events which happened in cities.
D. ...stories about gods and heroes.
E. ...events of everday life like a father and son after a hunt.

4.   The word **theatre** comes from

A.   ...a Roman word meaning, "viewing position".
B.   ...an English word meaning, "seeing place".
C.   ...a Roman word meaning, "stage".
D.   ...a Greek word meaning, "seeing place".
E.   ...a Greek word meaning, "scenery".

5.   What new developments did the Romans introduce into their theatre productions ?

A.   They built stages in fields and hills.
B.   They provided benches for the audience
C.   They provided a curtain and trap-doors.
D.   They used cranes to lower actors on to the stage.
E.   They were the first to introduce painted scenery.

6.   Why did actors and musicians have to take to the roads in the sixth century ?

A.   To take their plays to a wider audience.
B.   To give them opportunities to become better actors.
C.   To get away from being terrorised by the authorities.
D.   The fall of the Roman Empire led to the decline in the theatre.
E.   They weren't being paid in Rome.

7.   For how long did the wandering bands of actors and minstrels travel around from town to town ?

A.   For days on end.
B.   For a year.
C.   For a week.
D.   For 500 years.
E.   Until the sixth century.

8.   In the last paragraph what made the church change its attitude to drama and plays.

A.   Drama was a way to make the stories from the bible real.
B.   Drama could be used to convert pagans.
C.   Drama was a means of raising money to build churches.
D.   Drama was a way of bringing people into churches.
E.   Drama had become a favourable form of entertainment.

9. Which **TWO** acts of drama did the wandering bands of minstrels and musicians carry out ?

A. Songs and stories
B. Recitations and poems.
C. Plays and mimes.
D. Comedy and songs
E. Adventure stories and comedy acts.

10. Which of these is closest in meaning to **"primitive"** in **line 24** ?

A. outstanding
B. extraordinary
C. rudimentary
D. complex
E. cheap

The following passage contains a number of mistakes. You have to find the mistakes. On each line there is either _one_ mistake or _no_ mistake. Find the group of words in which there is a mistake and mark the letter for it on your answer sheet. If there is no mistake, mark N.

First, look for the _spelling_ mistakes.

11. The members / of these *guilds* / took over the / responsability for
     A   B   C   D   N

12. presenting religius / plays on / church feast days. / The plays
           A   B   C   D   N

13. were staged / on platforms / called *mansions* / in the market
         A   B   C   D   N

14. places. Each / guild chose / a diferent story / from the bible.
         A   B   C   D   N

15. They were / sometimes performed / on wheelled / stages which
         A   B   C   D   N

16. moved around / the town, so that / by waiting at / one point a
         A   B   C   D   N

17. spectator could / see the hole / series, or he / could follow
          A   B   C   D   N

18. his favorite play / around the town / and see it / several times.
           A   B   C   D   N

4.

19. These plays were | known as | Mystery plays. | There were also
          A   B   C   D   N

20. Mirakle plays | about the | lives of saints | and Morality.
       A   B   C   D   N

Now look for _punctuation_ mistakes.

21. These plays | showed the struggle? | between the | forces of Good
       A   B   C   D   N

22. and Evil. | manuscripts of some | of these plays | have been
       A   B   C   D   N

23. preserved and | they show | that the plays | we're exciting,
       A   B   C   D   N

24. realistic and | often humorous. | The professionals | ! also
       A   B   C   D   N

25. staged some, | of the more popular | religious plays | but for
       A   B   C   D   N

26. the most part | they presented | Popular comedies | and farces
       A   B   C   D   N

27. with a lot | of action, and | coarse humour. | In time these
       A   B   C   D   N

28. professionals | ceased performing | in the streets | in favour
       A   B   C   D   N
of the courtyards of inns.

Read this passage and answer the questions which follow. If there are any words you don't understand you may find them in the Glossary at the end of the test.

THE HAPPENING

1.   A farm horse named Charles was led to the town one day by its owner, to be shod. He would have been shod and brought back home without incident if it hadn't been for Eva, a duck, who was always hanging about the kitchen door of the farmhouse,

5.   eavesdropping, and never got anything quite right. Her farm mates said of her that she had two mouths but only one ear. On the day that Charles was led away to the smithy, Eva went quacking about the farm, excitedly telling the other animals that Charles had been taken to town to be shot.

10.   " They're executing an innocent horse !" cried Eva. "He's a hero ! He's a martyr ! He died to make us free !"
"He was the greatest horse in the world," sobbed a sentimental hen.
"He just seemed like old Charley to me," said a realistic cow. "Let's not get into a moony mood."

15.   "He was wonderful !" cried a gullible goose.
"What did he ever do ? " asked the goat.
Eva, who was as inventive as she was accurate, turned on her lively imagination. "It was butchers who led him to be shot !" she shrieked. "They would have cut our throats while we slept if it hadn't

20.   been for Charles."
         "I didn't see any butchers, and I can see a burnt-out firefly on a moonless night," said a barn owl. "I didn't see any butchers, and I can hear a mouse walk across the moss."
         "We must build a memorial to Charles the Great, who saved

25.   our lives," quacked Eva. And all the birds and beasts in the barnyard except the wise owl, the sceptical goat, and the realistic cow set about building a memorial.
         Just then the farmer appeared in the lane, leading Charles, whose shoes glinted in the sunlight.

30.   It was lucky that Charles was not alone, for the memorial builders might have set upon him with clubs and stones for replacing their hero with just plain old Charley. It was lucky, too, that they could not reach the barn owl, who quickly perched upon the weathervane of the barn, for none is so exasperating as he who

35.   is right.
         The sentimental hen and the gullible goose were the ones who finally called attention to the real culprit, Eva, the one-eared duck with two mouths. The others set upon her for none is more unpopular then the bearer of sad tidings that turn out to be false.

40.   Eva had to listen to the criticism of all the other animals and was forced to wander around on her own working out what she was to do to get back in the good books of her previous friends. She decided that the best plan was to return to her former claim to fame which was laying eggs that had two yolks.

45.   It took a while for her rash and dangerous gossiping to be forgotten. Eventually her plan worked but the other animals were now wary about what she had to say.

29. The animals said that Eva **"had two mouths but only one ear."**
Which of the statements below is the best meaning for this.

A.   She talked a lot but did not listen carefully.
B.   She was deaf.
C.   She was secretive.
D.   She could only hear with one ear.
E.   She talked a lot to the other animals.

30. Which is the best ending for this sentence ?
In reality Charles was going to

A.   see the town.   B.   a show.
C.   be fitted with shoes.   D.   meet other ducks
E.   be shot.

31. Which is the best ending for the sentence below.
The story suggests that the memorial builders were

A.   really concerned.   B.   stupid and unkind.
C.   furious and threatening. D.   silly but well meaning.
E.   laughing and joking

32. Which **animal** could be described as nosey and imaginative and
rarely got anything right ?

A.   cow   B.   duck   C.   goat
D.   owl   E.   hen

33. Which **animals** did not agree to build a memorial for the horse ?

A.   cow, duck and goat   B.   duck, goat and owl
C.   cow, goat and owl   D.   goose, duck and hen
E.   horse, cow and goat

34. Which of the **animals** had the best hearing and eyesight ?

A.   horse   B.   goat   C.   hen
D.   duck   E.   owl

SET 1 Blank Answer Sheets
ENGLISH Test 1
ENGLISH Test 2
ENGLISH Test 3

Instructions for completing the Answer Sheet.

1. You must concentrate fully when recording your answers.

    --take your time when recording your answers--

    --make sure you have the correct answer number--

    --make sure you select the correct letter, A, B, C, D, E or N--

2. Use a pencil to mark your answer, A, B, C, D, E or N.

3. Mark your answer like this---- (A) (B) (C) (D) (E) (N)

    (A) (B) (C) (D) (E) (N)

    (A) (B) (C) (D) (E) (N)

    ALWAYS USE A HORIZONTAL (—) LINE

4. DO NOT MARK like this-- (A) (B) (C) (D) (E) (N)

    (A) (B) (C) (D) (E) (N)

    (A) (B) (C) (D) (E) (N)

    (A) (B) (C) (D) (E) (N)

5. If you make a mistake, rub out the line, select the correct answer and draw a line through the correct letter.

6. It might be an idea to answer 5 questions at a time and then record these 5 answers all at the same time.

7. When reading the questions you record the answers on the question paper. When you have completed 5 questions on the question paper you then record these on the Answer sheet. Proceed to record another 5 questions.

ANSWER SHEETS — English Test 1

Please mark the boxes like (—), not like (╱). Rub out mistakes thoroughly.

Pages 2, 3 & 4.

1	(A) (B) (C) (D) (E)	6	(A) (B) (C) (D) (E)
2	(A) (B) (C) (D) (E)	7	(A) (B) (C) (D) (E)
3	(A) (B) (C) (D) (E)	8	(A) (B) (C) (D) (E)
4	(A) (B) (C) (D) (E)	9	(A) (B) (C) (D) (E)
5	(A) (B) (C) (D) (E)	10	(A) (B) (C) (D) (E)

Page 4
Spelling

11	(A) (B) (C) (D) (N)	16	(A) (B) (C) (D) (N)
12	(A) (B) (C) (D) (N)	17	(A) (B) (C) (D) (N)
13	(A) (B) (C) (D) (N)	18	(A) (B) (C) (D) (N)
14	(A) (B) (C) (D) (N)	19	(A) (B) (C) (D) (N)
15	(A) (B) (C) (D) (N)	20	(A) (B) (C) (D) (N)

Page 5
Punctuation

21	(A) (B) (C) (D) (N)	25	(A) (B) (C) (D) (N)
22	(A) (B) (C) (D) (N)	26	(A) (B) (C) (D) (N)
23	(A) (B) (C) (D) (N)	27	(A) (B) (C) (D) (N)
24	(A) (B) (C) (D) (N)	28	(A) (B) (C) (D) (N)

Pages 6, 7, 8 & 9.

29	(A) (B) (C) (D) (E)	36	(A) (B) (C) (D) (E)
30	(A) (B) (C) (D) (E)	37	(A) (B) (C) (D) (E)
31	(A) (B) (C) (D) (E)	38	(A) (B) (C) (D) (E)
32	(A) (B) (C) (D) (E)	39	(A) (B) (C) (D) (E)
33	(A) (B) (C) (D) (E)	40	(A) (B) (C) (D) (E)
34	(A) (B) (C) (D) (E)	41	(A) (B) (C) (D) (E)
35	(A) (B) (C) (D) (E)	42	(A) (B) (C) (D) (E)

Pages 10, 11 & 12.

43	(A) (B) (C) (D) (E)	49	(A) (B) (C) (D) (E)
44	(A) (B) (C) (D) (E)	50	(A) (B) (C) (D) (E)
45	(A) (B) (C) (D) (E)	51	(A) (B) (C) (D) (E)
46	(A) (B) (C) (D) (E)	52	(A) (B) (C) (D) (E)
47	(A) (B) (C) (D) (E)	53	(A) (B) (C) (D) (E)
48	(A) (B) (C) (D) (E)	54	(A) (B) (C) (D) (E)
		55	(A) (B) (C) (D) (E)

Pages 13 & 14
General Section

56 (a)	(A) (B) (C) (D)	58 (b)	(A) (B) (C) (D)
(b)	(A) (B) (C) (D)	59 (a)	(A) (B) (C) (D)
57 (a)	(A) (B) (C) (D)	(b)	(A) (B) (C) (D)
(b)	(A) (B) (C) (D)	60 (a)	(A) (B) (C) (D)
58 (a)	(A) (B) (C) (D)	(b)	(A) (B) (C) (D)

Multiple Choice English
Test 1 Answer Key.

CHRISTMAS EVE
1. C
2. E
3. B
4. C
5. A
6. B
7. D
8. B
9. E
10. D

Spelling
11. A--woken
12. A--generosity
13. N
14. D--route
15. B--decorated
16. D--our
17. A--neighbour's
18. B--wheaten
19. A--putting
20. N

Punctuation
21. N
22. A--capital I
23. A--capital Danny
24. C--no apostrophe
25. B--no question mark
26. C--What
27. C--tree's
28. A--no exclamation mark

FLIGHTY BIRD
29. A
30. E
31. B
32. D
33. B
34. C
35. C
36. B
37. D
38. C
39. D
40. A
41. B
42. C

GERMS
43. D
44. E
45. E
46. D
47. A
48. D
49. D
50. E
51. D
52. D
53. A
54. D
55. C

General Section
	(a)		(b).	
56.	B		D	
57.	C		C	
58.	C		C	
59.	B		B	
60.	B		C	

Multiple Choice English

Test 2 Answer Key.

DRAMA HISTORY

1. D
2. B
3. E
4. D
5. C
6. D
7. D
8. A
9. E
10. C

Spelling

11. D--responsibility
12. A--religious
13. N
14. C--different
15. C--wheeled
16. N
17. B--whole
18. A--favourite
19. N
20. A--Miracle

Punctuation

21. B--no question mark
22. B--Manuscripts
23. D--no apostrophe
24. D--no exclamation mark
25. A--no comma
26. C--popular
27. B--no comma
28. N

THE HAPPENING

29. A
30. C
31. C
32. B
33. C
34. E
35. A
36. C
37. E
38. D
39. C
40. B
41. D
42. C

TOMMY'S SEARCH

43. D
44. C
45. C
46. D
47. E
48. B
49. E
50. C
51. B
52. D
53. C
54. B
55. D

General Section

56.	(a)	C	(b).	B
57.	(a)	B	(b).	C
58.	(a)	C	(b).	B
59.	(a)	D	(b).	C
60.	(a)	A	(b).	D

Multiple Choice English

Test 3 Answer Key.

BAND AID

1. A
2. D
3. D
4. E.
5. C
6. B
7. B
8. C
9. E
10. C

Spelling

11. A--critics
12. B--live
13. C--television
14. B--Millions
15. A--cities
16. N
17. A--surpassed
18. C--satellite
19. A--estimated
20. D--broadcasts

Punctuation

21. D--he
22. B--no full stop
23. A--no question mark
24. D--Robert
25. B--no speech mark
26. C--comma needed
27. D--no exclamation mark
28. B--capital I

DEAF BUT ABLE

29. B
30. D
31. C
32. D
33. C
34. A
35. E
36. B
37. C
38. C
39. B
40. D
41. A
42. D

EAT A KUNGRY

43. B
44. E
45. A
46. E
47. C
48. B
49. E
50. A
51. D
52. C
53. D
54. E
55. D

General Section

	(a)		(b).	
56.	(a)	C	(b).	C
57.	(a)	A	(b).	C
58.	(a)	C	(b).	B
59.	(a)	C	(b).	C
60.	(a)	D	(b).	B

English Test 2

Please mark the boxes like (—), not like (╱). Rub out mistakes thoroughly.

Pages 2, 3 & 4.

1	(A) (B) (C) (D) (E)	6	(A) (B) (C) (D) (E)
2	(A) (B) (C) (D) (E)	7	(A) (B) (C) (D) (E)
3	(A) (B) (C) (D) (E)	8	(A) (B) (C) (D) (E)
4	(A) (B) (C) (D) (E)	9	(A) (B) (C) (D) (E)
5	(A) (B) (C) (D) (E)	10	(A) (B) (C) (D) (E)

Pages 4 & 5

Spelling

11	(A) (B) (C) (D) (N)	16	(A) (B) (C) (D) (N)
12	(A) (B) (C) (D) (N)	17	(A) (B) (C) (D) (N)
13	(A) (B) (C) (D) (N)	18	(A) (B) (C) (D) (N)
14	(A) (B) (C) (D) (N)	19	(A) (B) (C) (D) (N)
15	(A) (B) (C) (D) (N)	20	(A) (B) (C) (D) (N)

Page 5

Punctuation

21	(A) (B) (C) (D) (N)	25	(A) (B) (C) (D) (N)
22	(A) (B) (C) (D) (N)	26	(A) (B) (C) (D) (N)
23	(A) (B) (C) (D) (N)	27	(A) (B) (C) (D) (N)
24	(A) (B) (C) (D) (N)	28	(A) (B) (C) (D) (N)

Pages 7, 8 & 9.

29	(A) (B) (C) (D) (E)	36	(A) (B) (C) (D) (E)
30	(A) (B) (C) (D) (E)	37	(A) (B) (C) (D) (E)
31	(A) (B) (C) (D) (E)	38	(A) (B) (C) (D) (E)
32	(A) (B) (C) (D) (E)	39	(A) (B) (C) (D) (E)
33	(A) (B) (C) (D) (E)	40	(A) (B) (C) (D) (E)
34	(A) (B) (C) (D) (E)	41	(A) (B) (C) (D) (E)
35	(A) (B) (C) (D) (E)	42	(A) (B) (C) (D) (E)

Pages 10, 11, 12 & 13.

43	(A) (B) (C) (D) (E)	49	(A) (B) (C) (D) (E)
44	(A) (B) (C) (D) (E)	50	(A) (B) (C) (D) (E)
45	(A) (B) (C) (D) (E)	51	(A) (B) (C) (D) (E)
46	(A) (B) (C) (D) (E)	52	(A) (B) (C) (D) (E)
47	(A) (B) (C) (D) (E)	53	(A) (B) (C) (D) (E)
48	(A) (B) (C) (D) (E)	54	(A) (B) (C) (D) (E)
		55	(A) (B) (C) (D) (E)

Pages 13 & 14

General Section

56 (a)	(A) (B) (C) (D)	58 (b)	(A) (B) (C) (D)
(b)	(A) (B) (C) (D)	59 (a)	(A) (B) (C) (D)
57 (a)	(A) (B) (C) (D)	(b)	(A) (B) (C) (D)
(b)	(A) (B) (C) (D)	60 (a)	(A) (B) (C) (D)
58 (a)	(A) (B) (C) (D)	(b)	(A) (B) (C) (D)

English Test 3

Please mark the boxes like (—), not like (╱). Rub out mistakes thoroughly.

Pages 2, 3 & 4

1	(A)(B)(C)(D)(E)	6	(A)(B)(C)(D)(E)
2	(A)(B)(C)(D)(E)	7	(A)(B)(C)(D)(E)
3	(A)(B)(C)(D)(E)	8	(A)(B)(C)(D)(E)
4	(A)(B)(C)(D)(E)	9	(A)(B)(C)(D)(E)
5	(A)(B)(C)(D)(E)	10	(A)(B)(C)(D)(E)

Pages 4
Spelling

11	(A)(B)(C)(D)(N)	16	(A)(B)(C)(D)(N)
12	(A)(B)(C)(D)(N)	17	(A)(B)(C)(D)(N)
13	(A)(B)(C)(D)(N)	18	(A)(B)(C)(D)(N)
14	(A)(B)(C)(D)(N)	19	(A)(B)(C)(D)(N)
15	(A)(B)(C)(D)(N)	20	(A)(B)(C)(D)(N)

Page 5
Punctuation

21	(A)(B)(C)(D)(N)	25	(A)(B)(C)(D)(N)
22	(A)(B)(C)(D)(N)	26	(A)(B)(C)(D)(N)
23	(A)(B)(C)(D)(N)	27	(A)(B)(C)(D)(N)
24	(A)(B)(C)(D)(N)	28	(A)(B)(C)(D)(N)

Pages 7, 8 & 9.

29	(A)(B)(C)(D)(E)	36	(A)(B)(C)(D)(E)
30	(A)(B)(C)(D)(E)	37	(A)(B)(C)(D)(E)
31	(A)(B)(C)(D)(E)	38	(A)(B)(C)(D)(E)
32	(A)(B)(C)(D)(E)	39	(A)(B)(C)(D)(E)
33	(A)(B)(C)(D)(E)	40	(A)(B)(C)(D)(E)
34	(A)(B)(C)(D)(E)	41	(A)(B)(C)(D)(E)
35	(A)(B)(C)(D)(E)	42	(A)(B)(C)(D)(E)

Pages 11, 12 & 13.

43	(A)(B)(C)(D)(E)	49	(A)(B)(C)(D)(E)
44	(A)(B)(C)(D)(E)	50	(A)(B)(C)(D)(E)
45	(A)(B)(C)(D)(E)	51	(A)(B)(C)(D)(E)
46	(A)(B)(C)(D)(E)	52	(A)(B)(C)(D)(E)
47	(A)(B)(C)(D)(E)	53	(A)(B)(C)(D)(E)
48	(A)(B)(C)(D)(E)	54	(A)(B)(C)(D)(E)
		55	(A)(B)(C)(D)(E)

Pages 13 & 14
General Section

56	(a) (A)(B)(C)(D)	58	(b) (A)(B)(C)(D)
	(b) (A)(B)(C)(D)	59	(a) (A)(B)(C)(D)
57	(a) (A)(B)(C)(D)		(b) (A)(B)(C)(D)
	(b) (A)(B)(C)(D)	60	(a) (A)(B)(C)(D)
58	(a) (A)(B)(C)(D)		(b) (A)(B)(C)(D)

35. Which **TWO** animals discovered who it was who spread the rumour that Charles the horse was to be shot ?

A. The goose and the hen. B. The goat and the goose.
C. The hen and the goat. D. The owl and the goose.
E. The cow and the goose.

36. Which of these statements is **True** ?

A. The farmer was taking Charles to the town to be shot.
B. Charles died to save the other animals.
C. Charles went to the blacksmith to be shod.
D. Charles stopped the butchers from cutting the animals' throats.
E. Charles became a martyr and was a hero.

37. When Charles returned to the farm where was the owl ?

A. On its perch in the barn.
B. High up in a fir tree.
C. Perched on the chimney of the farmhouse.
D. Feeding with the other birds in the farmyard.
E. Perched on the weathervane.

38. What was unusual about the eggs that the duck was going to lay ?

A. They were smaller than hens' eggs.
B. They were bigger than hens' eggs.
C. They were green in colour.
D. They had two yolks.
E. They were laid in twos.

39. Another word that sounds like the **yolk** of an egg is **yoke**. What is a **yoke** ?

A. The white of an egg.
B. A farmyard tool.
C. A wooden frame placed across two animals to keep them together.
D. A steel bar which joins the back of a car to a trailer.
E. The young of a farmyard bird such as a hen, a duck or a turkey.

40. What was the reaction of the other animals to Eva, the duck at the end of the story ?

A. They trusted her completely.
B. They were suspicious about what she would say.
C. They hadn't forgotten her gossiping.
D. They walked around along with her.
E. They helped here overcome her gossiping problem.

41. In the last paragraph the words, **rash, dangerous** and **previous** are used. What **"part of speech"** are these words ?

A. nouns   B. pronouns   C. verbs
D. adjectives E. adverbs

42. Why was Eva, the duck, hanging about the kitchen door ?

A. To get any food that would be thrown out from the kitchen.
B. To lay eggs close to the house.
C. To listen for any information that came from the kitchen.
D. To keep an eye on what the other animals were doing.
E. To avoid meeting the other farmyard animals.

Read this passage and answer the questions which follow. If there are any words you don't understand you may find them in the Glossary at the end of the test.

TOMMY'S SEARCH

1.   It was night when he at last found the building he was looking for. He had of course thought that the family he knew lived in it alone but it was as crowded with strangers as a bus depot or a wharf. A man stood at an inner door letting people in and then
5.   shutting it so that they disappeared abruptly. Then, as suddenly, the door was flung open again and quite a different crowd poured out. Tommy could not understand it but when he asked the man if the family he knew lived there, the man said, "Get in; tenth floor," and he was pushed into a tiny cell along with a dozen other people.
10. The door was shut on them, the man pressed a button in the wall and the little wooden cell shot upwards with a sickening lurch.
     Before Tommy could get over the shock, it had come to a stop, the door was flung open and the man waved him out. "Number one hundred and two," he said, shut the door and disappeared.

9.

15.   Now Tommy was in the heart of the building. He looked about him and saw nothing but shut doors. He went up close to them to study the numbers and finally found one that had 102 on it in brass letters. He banged and hammered on it for quite a while before it was opened by a tall man in white trousers and a high-collared
20. white coat. "Why are you banging, idiot - don't you see the bell ?" he shouted.

      Tommy looked up to see if there was a bell hanging from the lintel but there was nothing there. "No," he said in a low voice, "where is it ?"

25.   "Here, fool," said the man angrily and, putting his finger on a white button beside the door frame, made it scream suddenly and shrilly. "Who are you and what do you want ?"

      "I want to see the Leader," Tommy whispered, staring past the man into the brightly lit room with its carpeted floor, large pieces of
30. furniture and bright pictures and mirrors and flowers. He became conscious of his dirty feet in their dusty sandals and wondered how he could ever step into that room in such a condition.

      The man at the door had no intention of letting him do so. "The Leader? Who sent you to meet him? Have you a letter ? "

35.   Tommy felt in his pocket for the bit of paper. "Here I have his name and address."

      "Who gave it to you ?"

      "He gave it to me."

      "Don't tell lies."

40.   "It is true. When he came to Bahl, I washed his car for him, and he told me to come and see him when I came to Bombay."

      The doorman opened up the piece of paper on which was written a message which wasn't easy to read. The man told Tommy to stay at the door as he went inside. Tommy heard voices and then
45. an almighty cheer. The Leader eventually appeared at the door and hugged Tommy who was carried into this most beautiful room.

      The doorman was ordered to prepare a hearty feast as the Leader informed Tommy that he was his uncle and Tommy was to live with him.

43. Which phrase from the **first paragraph** tells us that the inner door closed quickly ?

A.   ...lived in it alone.
B.   ...crowded with strangers.
C.   ...a different crowd poured out.
D.   ...they disappeared abruptly.
E.   ...an inner door letting people in.

44. Which phrase from the **first paragraph** that tells us how quickly people came out of the inner door ?

A. ...lived in it alone.
B. ...crowded with strangers.
C. ...a different crowd poured out.
D. ...they disappeared abruptly.
E. ...an inner door letting people in.

45. Which word between **lines 25 and 30** tells us that Tommy was looking at the room intensely ?

A. angrily   B. suddenly   C. staring
D. scream   E. whispered

46. Why was Tommy worried about going into the room ?

A. He was afraid of the bell.
B. He was scared of the doorman.
C. He didn't like the bright lights.
D. He had dirty feet and dusty sandals.
E. He thought it was the wrong room.

47. When Tommy found the building he was looking for, he was surprised because

A. it was a slum.   B. it was a palace.
C. it looked magnificent.   D. it was a bungalow.
E. it was a block of flats.

48. What was the tiny wooden cell that Tommy stepped into in the second paragraph ?

A. an hotel room   B. an elevator
C. a store room   D. a sauna
E. a bedroom

49. When Tommy said he wanted to meet the Leader, he probably whispered because

A. he did not want the neighbours to hear him.
B. he was overwhelmed by his recent experiences.
C. he had caught a cold.
D. he was exhausted.
E. he was afraid of the angry doorman.

50. Tommy was unfamiliar with

A. electric switches.
B. electric lights.
C. electric doorbells.
D. doorbells.
E. washing cars.

51. How is the building that Tommy entered described ?

A. ...a low, dark and drab building.
B. ...as crowded as a bus depot.
C. ...bright, airy and friendly.
D. ...stood on its own in the countryside.
E. ...a large building with all the doors open.

52. How do we know that the man at the door of room 102 was **not** friendly ?

A. He answered any questions put to him in a friendly manner.
B. He was dressed in shabby clothes.
C. He told visitors how to get to different places.
D. He spoke in a loud and angry way.
E. He banged and hammered the door.

53. Why did the journey in the wooden cell leave Tommy in a state of shock ?

A. The cell was so small and cramped.
B. The cell felt like a prison.
C. The door had been closed and the cell hurtled up.
D. The door flew open and people fell out.
E. There was a large crowd in the cell.

54. The words, **understand, shot, shut** and **pushed** are used in the second paragraph. What type of words are they ?

A. nouns   B. verbs   C. adjectives
D. adverbs   E. pronouns

55. Which of the following words is the best meaning for the word **"abruptly"** as used in **line 5** ?

A. frequently   B. clearly   C. effectively
D. suddenly   E. completely

General Section
To answer these questions, you may have to think about the passages you have read. Look back at these if you need to. Look also at the Index and Glossary.

56. (a) In which part of this test would you find a list of words and their definitions.

A. Passage "Tommy's Search"   B. INDEX
C. GLOSSARY   D. General Section

(b). What is the best description for the type of writing in the first passage, **"DRAMA HISTORY"**, of this test ?

A. rhyming   B. non-fictional
C. fictional   D. illegible

57. (a) Words which are used to take the **place of nouns** in sentences are called

A. conjunctions   B. pronouns
C. nouns   D. adjectives

(b) Which word in the Glossary means the same as **"dubious"** ?

A. legendary   B. sentimental
C. sceptical   D. conscious

58. (a) The purpose of the INDEX page is

A. Find meanings of words.
B. Find the important words.
C. List the pages on which key words can be found.
D. Shows the reader where the illustrations are.

In each of the following questions you have to choose the *best word* or *group of words* to complete this passage so that it makes sense. Choose one of the answers and mark the letter on the answer sheet.

The common people stood in the courtyard and watched the actors perform on a raised wooden stage.

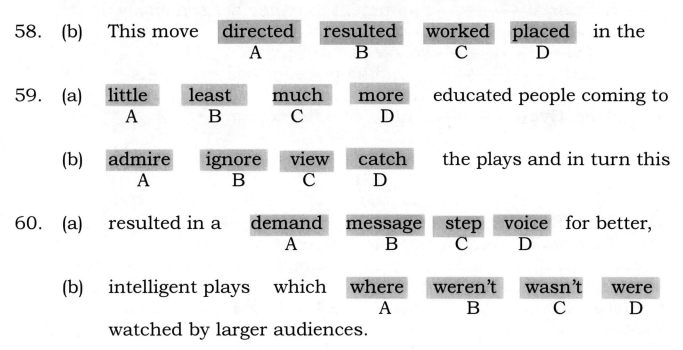

58. (b) This move directed   resulted   worked   placed in the
                   A   B   C   D

59. (a) little   least   much   more educated people coming to
       A   B   C   D

(b) admire   ignore   view   catch   the plays and in turn this
       A   B   C   D

60. (a) resulted in a   demand   message   step   voice for better,
                    A   B   C   D

(b) intelligent plays which   where   weren't   wasn't   were
                              A   B   C   D

watched by larger audiences.

GLOSSARY

civilisation------------ society with high level of social standards
skene------------------- Greek word for changing room
legendary------------- famous in legends or stories
inspiration------------ brilliant idea
mechanical----------- performed by machines
minstrels------------- medieval singers or musicians
reciting--------------- repeat a poem, etc. aloud to an audience
banquets-------------- large formal dinners
eavesdropping------- listen secretly to a private conversation
quacking-------------- noise that a duck makes
sentimental----------romantic and emotional
gullible---------------- easily fooled or tricked
sceptical-------------- disbelieving and doubtful
memorial------------- monument to remember somebody or event
exasperating--------- annoying and irritating
yolks------------------- yellow parts of eggs
wharf------------------ a landing place for boats or ships
conscious-------------aware or alive to
primitive------------- crude, unrefined, simple

INDEX

15.

NEW TRANSFER TESTS

MULTIPLE-CHOICE

ENGLISH

Practice Test 3

Guidance for completing this Test.

1.   Read the passages carefully.

2.   Read the questions thoroughly.

3.   Read the answers carefully.

4.   Choose what you think is the correct answer carefully.

5.   Underline or circle the answer, immediately after the
     question.

6.   Transfer the LETTER **A,B,C,D,E** or **N** to the answer sheet.

7.   Make sure to mark the answer box like [—] not [✓].

8.   Check carefully that you have transferred your correct answer.

9 . This test lasts for **50 minutes.**

PUPIL'S NAME _____

TOTAL MARK (Out of 60)	

Read this passage and answer the questions which follow. If there are any words you don't understand you may find them in the Glossary at the end of the test.

BAND AID

1.   Bob Geldof was a musician from Ireland who worked with a band called the Boomtown Rats, which had one international hit single in 1979 called "I don't like Mondays". They were the number one band that year and Geldof had contacts with most of

5.   the rock stars at the time and was aware of the sporadic efforts by musicians to help the under-privileged Third World, eg. following the 1970 storm surge in East Pakistan (Bangladesh) and the country's independence.

        Musicians had organised a concert involving lots of people to

10. raise money to help overcome this disaster - the "Concert for Bangladesh". It was staged free by several famous rock groups, and raised several million dollars.

        Bob Geldof, like many other people in 1984, was appalled by the plight of the Ethiopians and the fact that the famine

15. remained virtually unknown to the outside world until a British television crew led by reporter Michael Buerk tripped over it. Buerk's film showed the enormity of the disaster, and painted a dismal, hell-like picture.

        Children were being selectively fed. Only those who had a

20. hope of surviving were permitted to join food queues. People were dying throughout the film. In the midst of this anarchy, the Ethiopian people went on trying to live in the camps which were overcrowded and without medical aid. Their honesty formed a striking contrast to the greed of most people viewing the show.

25.   Though starving, Ethiopian refugees would not touch food in open stores unless it was given to them. No one appeared to be doing anything to help them. The Ethiopian government had denied the existence of the drought and the international monitoring agencies had failed to bring it to world attention.

30.   Bob Geldof, a rock musician, was hardly the most obvious candidate to organize and lead the largest relief effort in history. Geldof began to organize and coerce, to put a group of musicians together to perform a record for the Christmas of 1984, the profits of which were donated to Ethiopian relief. The band was called Band

30. Aid, an obvious play on words, chosen because the name would make people aware of the futility of this one act of charity in overcoming famine. In the end Geldof managed to convince all associated with the record to donate their services free. The proceeds of the record were to be put into a special fund to be

40. distributed for relief aid as the committee saw fit.
        The record contained the song "Do they know it's Christmas" on one side, and some messages from rock stars on the other. It cost £1.30 and reached "number one" the day it was released, six weeks before Christmas. Within weeks it was selling 300,000 copies

45. a day and utilising the printing facilities of every record factory in Britain, Ireland and Europe to meet demand. People bought 5 copies, kept one and gave the rest back for resale; they were used as Christmas cards, sold in restaurants and replaced meat displays in butchers' shops.

Answer the following questions. Look back over the passage. You should choose the _best_ answer and mark its letter on your answer sheet.

1. This passage is mainly about

A. Geldof's efforts to help the Ethiopian people.
B. natural disasters.
C. efforts to help poor countries.
D. the famine in Ethiopia.
E. making a number one pop song.

2. Which of the following is **TRUE** ?

A. The record was performed for the Christmas of 1978.
B. Buerk gave Band Aid its name.
C. There was only one Band Aid group.
D. Boomtown Rats was the number one band in 1979.
E. The record "I don't like Mondays" was a hit in 1984.

3. Which of the following is **FALSE** ?

A. Geldof was an Irish musician with the Boomtown Rats.
B. Michael Buerk was a reporter with the BBC.
C. During the famine in 1984, not all children were given food.
D. The international monitoring agencies drew attention to the famine in Ethiopia in 1984.
E. There were 300,000 records sold per day.

4. How did the world get to know about the Ethiopian famine ?

A. Bob Geldof was the first to bring the famine to world attention.
B. The Ethiopian government appealed to the world for help.
C. The neighbouring states to Ethiopa first reported the famine.
D. The record "Do they know it's Christmas" first made it known.
E. The BBC reporter Michael Beurk was the first to film the disaster.

2.

5. The Ethiopian government denied the existence of something.
   What was this ?

A. The famine.
B. Starving children.
C. The drought.
D. That children were dying.
E. The disaster in Bangladesh.

6. How many copies of Band Aid's record "Do you know it's Christmas"
   were sold in a **WEEK** ?
A. £ 1.30
B. 2,100,000
C. 300,000
D. 15 million
E. 25

7. **Two ADJECTIVES** are used to describe the picture that the TV
   programme showed of the famine.
   What are these adjectives ?

A. under-privileged and several
B. dismal and hell-like
C. medical and famous
D. honesty and disaster
E. enormity and unknown

8. In the **first paragraph** what was it that Bob Geldof was aware of ?

A. The name of his band.
B. Rock stars had organised a concert for East Pakistan.
C. The occasional efforts by musicians to help the Third World.
D. The 1970 storm.
E. Raising several million dollars.

9. Which body was to distribute the proceeds from the record made by
   Bob Geldof and Band Aid.

A. The East Pakistan government.
B. The Ethiopian government.
C. Volunteer aid workers.
D. The Band Aid musicians.
E. A committee formed from the band, "Band Aid".

10. In which three unusual ways were copies of the record, **"Do they know it's Christmas "**, sold ?

A. ...on the internet, from door to door and in supermarkets.
B. ...in churches, hotels and leisure centres.
C. ...as Christmas cards, in restaurants and butchers' shop.
D. ...in pubs, shops and cafes.
E. ...in record shops, at train stations and in printers.

The following passage contains a number of mistakes. You have to find the mistakes. On each line there is either _one_ mistake or _no_ mistake. Find the group of words in which there is a mistake and mark the letter for it on your answer sheet. If there is no mistake, mark N.

First, look for the _spelling_ mistakes.

11. The critacs said   that it could   not be done.   But Bob did it !
       A   B   C   D   N

12. In 1985 he   organized a life concert. It was the   first concert
       A   B   C   D   N

13. of its kind and ran for 17 hours on telavision   using satellite
       A   B   C   D   N

14. hook-ups. Milions of fans attended numerous   concerts held
       A   B   C   D   N

15. in citys from London to Moscow to Melbourne to Philadelphia.
       A   B   C   D   N

16. There were 82,000 fans at Wembley in London   but this was
       A   B   C   D   N

17. surpased by   99,000 fans who turned up in Philadelphia.
       A   B   C   D   N

18. The various shows were linked by satelite   and Television.
       A   B   C   D   N

19. An estimatted crowd of 400 million viewers   from over 60
       A   B   C   D   N

20. countries   watched   the live   broadkasts.
       A   B   C   D   N

4.

Now look for _punctuation_ mistakes.

21. William gave | him a dark look. | As in imagination | He ejected
     A   B   C   D   N

22. him from the | lecture. sending | him flying | through the
         A   B   C   D   N

23. door? and | half-way down the | flight of stairs | that was just
        A   B   C   D   N

24. outside the | lecture-room. | Having got rid | of robert, he turned
       A   B   C   D   N

25. to his mother, | "preparing | aggressively to | defend at great
       A   B   C   D   N

26. length the state | of his hair, face, | hands .suit | and boots.
          A   B   C   D   N

27. But instead of | attacking these | very vulnerable | points! his
         A   B   C   D   N

28. mother said, | "i have an | invitation to | tea tomorrow. "
        A   B   C   D   N

Read this passage and answer the questions which follow. If there are any words you don't understand you may find them in the Glossary at the end of the test.

DEAF BUT ABLE

1.   Living two doors from me when I was twelve years old, and being my closest friend at the time was a boy called Dicky Fitt. Dicky was deaf and dumb but this problem, so far as could be seen, made very little difference to his life among us boys. He had to fit
5. into our world like every other boy has to and he fitted without being noticeably different. I must say that he was exceptionally gifted at following your lips and when we were gathered together under the corner lamp-post telling tales, he would often be the first to burst out laughing at the end.
10.   His being dumb made no apparent difference to any of us since we were a rather healthy bunch of active lads and each one listened to no one but himself, so Dicky wouldn't have been heard - except by himself - had he been able to speak. Also, when he wished to make himself understood, Dicky was energetic about it and

15. would leave you in no doubt as to what was in his mind. Nor did his muteness mark him in any way as being inferior among us; on the contrary, we were inclined to consider him as specially gifted, in that he could speak with his hands.

On Saturdays Dicky and I used to earn ourselves a shilling
20. apiece by hauling the little two-wheeled truck of coal from Mundy's Yard to neighbours' homes. At the end of our labours we used to go to Ma Walsh's pie-shop in Dobbsgate. She used to sell steak-and-kidney pies, fresh from the oven, crammed with the most tender meat - all prime, juicy and onion-flavoured. We each bought a
25. sixpenny one and ate them walking along the street. "When I'm a millionaire," Dicky used to make signs to me, swelling out his trouser-pockets, "I'll eat nothing but Ma Walsh's pies !"

Excitability and moodiness were the only two things which made Dicky different from normal boys. He had an intense capacity
30. for either of these. Playing football - at which he was very good - he would suddenly start to make loud squawking shrieks when pressing in on the other team's goalmouth. He was handicapped by not being able to hear the referee's whistle; and later, when being nagged for keeping on playing after the whistle had blown, he
35. would hang his head and sulk.

Or on occasional Friday evenings, if his mother did not arrive home at the accustomed time - there was only her and Dicky in the home and he would get the tea ready - he would be depressed beyond anything I could imagine. Dicky's mother was a hard-
40. working little woman who slaved away at the local tannery all week and on odd pay-days she might allow herself to be persuaded into having a glass of beer with her workmates before going home.

Now it happened that a speech specialist came to the school clinic one day and, after examining Dicky, sent word home to his
45. mother that, with her permission, he could arrange for the boy to go to an institution in the Midlands, where he would almost certainly learn how to speak.

Mrs. Fitt was excited about the prospect but not Dicky. He said that he wanted to stay where he was, and that he didn't want to
50. learn to speak any different from what he already knew. And I agreed with him, because I didn't want him to go away either; and I also felt that things wouldn't be the same between us once he learned to talk. Most of the neighbours said that it would be a shame for a mother to let her son go away to a strange place, but
55. the specialist convinced Mrs. Fitt that it was her duty to let him go and she took his advice.

Answer the following questions. Look back over the passage. You should choose the _best_ answer and mark its letter on your answer sheet.

29. When Dicky wanted to make himself understood he

A. ...shouted out loud.
B. ...spoke with his hands.
C. ...wrote it down on paper.
D. ...asked one of the boys to tell everyone.
E. ...danced on the street.

30. Dicky was able to understand the stories told under the lamp-post in the first paragraph because

A. ...one of his friends whispered them to him.
B. ...he had already read them in a book.
C. ...he heard the boys telling them.
D. ...he was able to read the lips of the reader.
E. ...his mother had told him the stories.

31. Dicky and his friend earned a shilling each on a Saturday

A. ...by selling newspapers on the street.
B. ...by delivering meat for the butcher.
C. ...by delivering coal to neighbours' houses.
D. ...by selling steak-and-kidney pies for Ma Walsh.
E. ...by washing cars for their neighbours.

32. Dicky got the tea ready on some Friday evenings when

A. ...his friends were coming to visit.
B. ...his father was at home.
C. ...he was really hungry and needed to eat.
D. ...his mother didn't come home at the usual time.
E. ...he was going out to play football.

33. Dicky's mother sent him to an institution

A. ...because she couldn't look after him at home.
B. ...because Dicky wanted to go to learn to talk.
C. ...because the specialist convinced her to send him.
D. ...because all her neighbours encouraged her to send him.
E. ...because Dicky always wanted to go away from home.

34.	Dicky and his friend got the steak-and-kidney pies

A.	...in a shop in Dobbsgate.
B.	...from the two-wheeled truck.
C.	...from the school canteen.
D.	...at the institution in the Midlands.
E.	...from Dicky's kitchen.

35.	Where did the author of this passage live ?

A.	In the Midlands.	B.	Beside the pie-shop.
C.	At Mundy's yard.	D.	Beside the football field.
E.	Two doors fom Dicky's house.

36.	How are the steak-and-kidney pies described ?

A.	gifted, large and juicy.
B.	prime, juicy and onion-flavoured.
C.	fresh, swelling and crammed.
D.	tender, tiny and tough.
E.	squawking, different and meat-flavoured.

37.	Apart from being deaf and dumb which other TWO things made
	Dicky different from normal boys ?

A.	a lame leg and bad eyesight.
B.	not able to laugh or cry.
C.	excitable and moody.
D.	depressed and not able to work.
E.	inferior and specially gifted.

38.	Why did the author of the passage feel that his relationship with
	Dicky wouldn't be the same after going to the institution?

A.	His friends wouldn't want to hang around with him.
B.	The author liked being able to speak to Dicky without reply.
C.	Dicky would be able to talk.
D.	They wouldn't be able to deliver coal.
E.	The neighbours would want Dicky to come back.

39.	The phrase **"specially gifted"** is used at the end of the second
	paragraph. Which is the **best meaning** for this phrase ?

A.	....receives a lot of presents.	B.	....brilliantly talented.
C.	....useless at sports.	D.	....skilled at sports.
E.	....excellent speaker.

40. Which of the following is the best meaning of the word, **"handicapped"** as used in the **fourth paragraph** ?

A. ....able to do all the things that normal people do.
B. ....not able to make loud squawking shrieks
C. ....able to hear and talk about the football.
D. ....being unable to carry out normal things.
E. ....being unable to go to the institution.

41. Where did Dicky's mother work ?

A. In the local tannery.   B. In the coal yard.
C. In Dicky's school.   D.   In Ma Walsh's shop.
E. In the institution.

42. An **"institution"** is

A. A food shop.
B. The local school.
C. A place for boys who behave badly.
D. Special school for handicapped pupils.
E. A society where prisoners are helped.

**Read this passage and answer the questions which follow.
If there are any words you don't understand you may find them
in the Glossary at the end of the test.**

EAT A KUNGRY

1.   Hunger stole up on me so slowly that at first I was not aware
of what hunger really meant. Hunger had always been more or less
at my elbow when I played but now I began to wake up at night to
find hunger standing at my bedside staring at me gauntly.

5.   The hunger I had known before this had been no hostile
stranger. It had been a normal hunger that had made me beg for
a crust of bread from time to time and when I had eaten it I was
satisfied. But this new hunger puzzled me, scared me, made me

10. angry. Whenever I ask for food now my mother would pour me a
cup of tea which would help for just a moment but a little later
I would feel hunger nudging my ribs, twisting my empty guts till
they ached. I would grow dizzy and my vision would dim. I hadn't
the energy to play and for the first time in my life I had to stop

15. and think of what was happening to me.
        One afternoon I complained, "Mama, I'm hungry."

9.

" Jump up and catch a kungry," she said, trying to make me
        laugh and forget.
"What's a kungry ?"
20. "It's what little boys eat when they get hungry," she said.
"What does it taste like ?"
"I don't know."
"Then why do you tell me to catch one ?"
"Because you told me you were hungry," she said smiling.
25. I sensed that she was teasing me and it made me angry.
"But I'm hungry. I want something to eat."
"You'll have to wait for there's nothing to eat," she told me but I
began to cry, pleading with her to get me food. She said that we had
to wait till God sent us some food.
30. In pain I asked, "When is He going to send it ?" My mother
didn't know and as she looked up from her ironing she had tears in
her eyes. She asked "Where's your father ?"
I stared at her in bewilderment. It was true that my father had
not come home to sleep for many days now and I could make as
35. much noise as I wanted. Though I had not known that he was
absent I had been glad that he had not been there to shout his
orders and rules at me. But it had never occurred to me that his
absence meant that there would be no food. I told my mother I
didn't know where my father was.
40. As the long days slowly moved along, the image of my father
became connected with those pangs of hunger in my stomach and
whenever I felt hunger I thought of him with anger and resentment.
My mother finally went to work as a cook and left me with my
brother alone in the flat each day with a loaf of bread and a big pot
45. of tea. When she returned in the evening she would be tired and
very low in spirits and she would cry a lot.
Sometimes when I was in despair, she would call to us and
talk to us for hours, telling us that we now had no father and that
our lives would be different from other children's that we must learn
50. as soon as possible to take care of ourselves, to dress ourselves, to
prepare our own food; that we must take on ourselves the
responsibility of the flat while she worked.
Half frightened, we would promise to carry out her wishes.
We did not understand what had happened between our father and
55. mother and the most these long talks did for us was to make us
vaguely afraid. Whenever we asked why father had left, she would
tell us that we were too young to know.

10.

43. Why did the author become angry ?

A. He was given a cup of tea.
B. He thought his mother was teasing him.
C. His father was living at home.
D. He woke up in the middle of the night.
E. His mother had become a cook.

44. Which TWO things happened to the author when he was very hungry ?

A. he became angry and excited.
B. he left school and worked in a shop.
C. he slept a lot and played football.
D. he asked for food and dreamed for food.
E. he grew dizzy and his vision would dim.

45. When did the author think of his father with resentment and anger ?

A. Whenever he felt very hungry.
B. When he came home from school.
C. When his father was at home.
D. When his mother gave him food.
E. When there was no food in the house.

46. Which tasks had the children to undertake when their mother told them that their father would not be coming home ?

A. ...washing dishes, ironing and shopping.
B. ...painting, gardening and cleaning the flat.
C. ...cooking, washing and running messages.
D. ...begging, ironing and dressing.
E. ...looking after themselves, dressing and preparing food.

47. According to the passage which of the following is **FALSE** ?

A. The author's mother gave him tea when he asked for food.
B. His father shouted orders and rules at him.
C. The family, mother, father and children lived together.
D. The author's mother worked as a cook.
E. The author didn't know where his father was.

11.

48. According to the passage which of the following is **TRUE** ?

A. The author had always plenty to eat.
B. The author's mother said that God would send food.
C. When the author was hungry his mother cooked steak.
D. The author was always happy.
E. The author never was in pain.

49. Which of the following is a **kungry** ?

A. ...a cup of tea and cake.
B. ...food that is fed to small boys and girls.
C. ...a loaf of crusty bread.
D. ...a tropical fruit on a tree.
E. ...something that the author was told to catch.

50. Which of the following best describes how the author's mother felt ?

A. ...very sad, depressed, exhausted.
B. ...friendly, lively, full of fun.
C. ...hard-working, helpful, bewildered.
D. ...rich, patient, irresponsible.
E. ...afraid, tired, hostile.

51. In the **last paragraph** what made the children afraid ?

A. ...the thought of their father coming home.
B. ...carrying out their mother's wishes.
C. ...their father and mother arguing.
D. ...the long talks they had with their mother.
E. ...the fact that they were young.

52. When had the author's mother tears in her eyes ?

A. When she was leaving her children in the flat.
B. When her husband left her.
C. When she was ironing clothes.
D. When she realised that she had no food.
E. When the author made a lot of noise.

53. In the **second paragraph** what satisfied the author's hunger ?

A. ...growing dizzy.   B. ...having no energy.
C. ...a cup of tea.   D. ...a crust of bread.
E. ...having weak vision.

54. Which of the following words in **line 11** are **nouns** ?

A. ...cup, which, hungry, my.
B. ...tea, still, storm, for.
C. ...of, would, storm, my.
D. ...hungry, storm, my, stomach.
E. ...cup, tea, storm, stomach.

55. The words **gauntly** and **slowly** are used in the first paragraph. What part of speech are they ?

A. verbs   B. nouns
C. pronouns   D. adverbs
E. adjectives

General Section
To answer these questions, you may have to think about the passages you have read. Look back at these if you need to. Look also at the Index and Glossary.

56. (a)   In which of the following would you find **fictional writing** ?

A. Reference Book   B. History text book
C. Novel   D. Biography

(b).   On which pages of the **INDEX** would you find names of people ?

A. pages 1, 2, 4.   B. pages 1, 5, 14.
C. pages 1, 5, 6.   D. pages 1, 5, 10.

57. (a)   In which section of the passage would you find **Ma Walsh's** name ?

A. DEAF BUT ABLE   B. BAND AID
C. EAT A KUNGRY   D. Punctuation

(b).   Which of the following is the best description of PUNCTUATION ?

A. Groups of sentences that have the same theme in a story.
B. Organises words into particular groups or parts of speech.
C. Signs or symbols which help to make sense of sentences.
D. Sequence of words which together give meaning.

13.

58. (a) In which publication would you find words which have similar meanings to related words?

A. Dictionary
C. Thesaurus

B. Diary
D. Bibliography

(b). What **"part of speech"** could be described as words which add information to verbs, adjectives and other adverbs ?

A. Adjectives
C. Interjections

B. Adverbs
D. Exclamations

59. (a) Which of the following is closest in meaning to the phrase **"pressing in on the other team's goalmouth "** as used in **line 32** of the passage, DEAF BUT ABLE ?

A. ...laying new grass in the pitch's goalmouth.
B. ...erecting the goalposts.
C. ...attacking the other team's goal area.
D. ...defending the other team's goal area.

(b). Which **THREE** words in the Glossary are **nouns** ?

A. apparent, capacity, utilising.
B. tannery, contrary, famine.
C. resentment, famine, institution.
D. anarchy, contrary, apparent.

60. (a) Which word in the GLOSSARY is closest in meaning to **self-reliance**?

A. anarchy
C. utilising

B. monitoring
D. independence

(b). In which of the sections of the Test would you find the characters, Bob Geldof and Michael Buerk and the country Bangladesh ?

A. EAT A KUNGRY
C. DEAF BUT ABLE

B. BAND AID
D. General section

14.

GLOSSARY

independence------ capable of acting for one's self or on one's own
famine-------------- severe shortage of food
anarchy------------ lawlessness and disorder
drought------------- lengthy period without rainfall
monitoring---------- checking, controlling, warning or keeping a record
donated------------- given to a charity or an organisation
utilising------------ making practical use of something or somebody
apparent------------ readily seen; obvious
contrary------------ complete opposite
capacity------------ able to contain; maximum amount held
tannery------------- place where animal hides are made into leather
institution---------- large important organisation; eg. university
bewilderment------- confusion
absence-------------- being away from work, school or home; not present
resentment---------- bitterness, ill will, grudge

INDEX